The Complete Rock & Pop Guitar Player

by Mick Barker, Rick Cardinali, Roger Day.

Book 2

Music Sales' complete catalogue describes thousands of titles and is available
in full colour sections by subject, direct from Music Sales Limited.
Please state your areas of interest and send a cheque/postal order for £1.50 for postage to:
Music Sales Limited, Newmarket Road, Bury St. Edmunds, Suffolk IP33 3YB.

Your Guarantee of Quality
As publishers, we strive to produce every book to
the highest commercial standards.
This book has been carefully designed to make playing from it a real pleasure.
Throughout, the printing and binding have been planned to ensure a sturdy,
attractive publication which should give years of enjoyment.
If your copy fails to meet our high standards, please inform us and
we will gladly replace it.

Printed in the United Kingdom by
J.B. Offset Printers (Marks Tey) Limited, Marks Tey, Essex.

Wise Publications
London/New York/Paris/Sydney/Copenhagen/Madrid

You don't have to learn to read music to play the songs in this book. If you wish, you can simply strum along to the songs as you did in Book I.

Reading Music Made Easy

The music we play is written on five equally spaced lines called a stave (staff).

Staves are divided into bars (or measures) by the use of a vertical line.

Each *bar* has a fixed number of *beats* in it. A *beat* is the natural tapping rhythm of a song. Most songs have four *beats* in each *bar*, and we can tap our feet or count along with these songs.

Occasionally, there are three *beats* in each *bar*, and we count like this:

How do we know the number of *beats* in a bar of music simply by looking at it?
At the beginning of every piece of music there is a time signature which gives us this information. It consists of two numbers, one above the other. The top number tells us how many beats there are in each bar, the lower number tells us the value of these beats as expressed in the musical notation which we use (we shall come to notes shortly).

In simple music which is used in these books we see the three most common time signatures

4
4 is often shown as **C**, or Common Time.

Once given, the *time signature* is not repeated, unless the *beat* changes within a song. This happens only occasionally in rock music.
The symbol we see at the beginning of each *stave* is called the *treble clef*.

There are other clefs, but the *treble clef* is used for all the songs in this book. What is a clef? Well, a clef fixes the *pitch* of a given note within a *stave*. The *treble clef* is used here because it fixes the most suitable *pitch* for singing the songs in these books.
In music there are various standard markings which can be used to abbreviate the layout. When we come to this sign

it tells us to go back to where this sign appears

(or, sometimes, when this does not appear, we return to the beginning) and repeat the section.

Sometimes we repeat the whole section, but the ending of the 'second time through' can be different from the first time. Thus we have what are called 1st and 2nd time bars (or a 3rd and 4th for that matter). Here is an example:

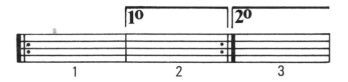

The first time through, we play bars 1 & 2. The second time we play bars 1 & 3.
We often see the letters D.C. & D.S. at the end of a stave line. D.C. (from the Italian *da capo*) tells us to return to the beginning ('top'). D.S. *(dal segno)* means return to the sign, ℘ . After these letters we see the words *al coda* (to the *coda*) or *al fine* (to the finish).
The *coda* is the end section of a song, usually short. Here is an example:

Here we play bars 1 – 3. We are then directed back to bar 2, and continue to bar 3, when the sign ⊕ above the bar line tells us to jump to the *coda* at bar 4.

Here is another example:

Play bars 1 – 4. Then return to bar 1, and continue to bar 2, where the word *Fine* (or end) tells us to stop. Sometimes coupled with the word *Fine* we see the sign ⌒ over a chord or note. This means you pause on the beat marked, letting the final chord ring. This is a very common ending.

%. means that you should repeat the preceding bar

is played.

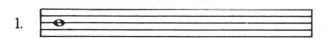

means that you should repeat the preceding two bars

NOTES – VALUES – TIES
Now we come to *notes* and their time values. The *notes* tell the player exactly *what to play, how to play it,* and *when to play it.*

Semibreve, (or whole note)

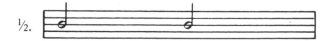

Minims, (or half notes)

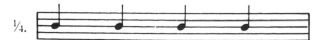

Crotchets, (or quarter notes)

Quavers, (or eighth notes)

Semiquavers, (or sixteenth notes)

The notes in each stave of the chart all add up to 4 beats, the beat being a crotchet.

So in a piece of music in  time we count 4 beats to the bar, each beat being one crotchet.

A bar in 2/4 time will contain two crotchet beats to the bar.

The same principle applies to 3/4 time:

Here we see a minim with a *dot* after it. The *dot* increases by a half the time value of any note after which it is placed.

Many guitar accompaniments consist of strumming 8 quavers to each bar of 4/4 time. We still count 4 crotchets, but to maintain an easy rhythm we count 1 & 2 & 3 & 4 &, each syllable being one quaver value (1/8)

or

Sometimes we see dotted quavers and semiquavers joined together. Again we count four, but the rhythm does not flow smoothly as with 8 quavers to the bar, and we count like this:

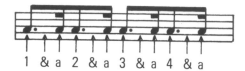

1 & a 2 & a 3 & a 4 & a

Just as notes tell us when to play, we have *rests* which tell us when *not* to play. There is a rest which corresponds in value to each type of note.

Semibreve	Minim	Crotchet	Quaver	Semiquaver

Similarly, dotted rests have the same time values as dotted notes.

A whole bar's rest is generally shown by a semibreve rest, whether or not the music is in 4/4 time.

Here is the scale of C major
A tone (T) is made up of 2 semitones (S/T) and semitones correspond to the frets on your guitar.
i.e. C to D is a tone or two frets
     E to F is a semitone or one fret.

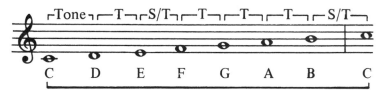

Tone T S/T T T T S/T
C   D   E   F   G   A   B   C

This is an *octave* and can be repeated up or down the stave. The first C is below the stave and we see that a *ledger line* runs through the note. This is an extension of the stave to accommodate the note. Here are more examples:

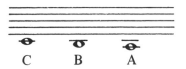

C   B   A

At the beginning of each stave line, we see, after the treble clef, the *key signature* of the music. This consists of sharps or flats or, in the case of C major or A minor none at all, and indicates that all notes against which they are set should be raised or lowered by a semitone.

Here, *all* Fs are to be raised by a semitone in all *octaves*.

Here, *all* Bs and Es are to be lowered by a semitone in all octaves.

It is necessary sometimes to insert sharps or flats that do not occur in the *key signatures,* they are called accidentals. In this case we put the sign before the individual note, and its effect lasts for *one bar only*. The natural sign ♮ is also used to countermand a sharp or flat given in the key signature. Again its effect is for one bar only:

or   or

Finally, we come to the curved line, which, in its various functions, will occur in these books.

It has the effect of joining together two notes.

When you see two notes of the same pitch tied together you simply play the first one and let it ring on through the note to which it is tied.

Another line often seen on vocal music is the syllable line:

ba - by   come back and stay

Here the line groups together notes to be sung on one syllable. Where the word is of two or more syllables, they are separated by a hyphen. Monosyllabic words simply have a straight line after them for the duration of the syllable line.

These are the outlines of reading and understanding simple music.

The songs, whether rock standards or up-to-date hits, will probably be familiar to you, so that by singing what you already know and matching it with the printed music you will understand the various combinations of notes.

Tablature Explained

The tablature stave comprises six lines, each representing a string on the guitar as illustrated.

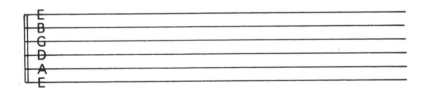

A number on any of the lines indicates, therefore, the string and fret on which a note should be played.

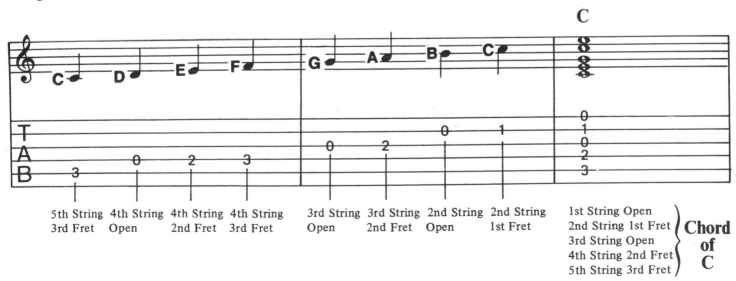

5th String	4th String	4th String	4th String	3rd String	3rd String	2nd String	2nd String	1st String Open
3rd Fret	Open	2nd Fret	3rd Fret	Open	2nd Fret	Open	1st Fret	2nd String 1st Fret

Chord of C:
1st String Open
2nd String 1st Fret
3rd String Open
4th String 2nd Fret
5th String 3rd Fret

Come Back And Stay
Words & Music: Jack Lee

The G Chord

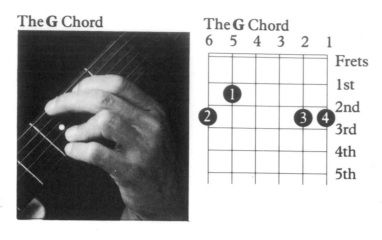

The G Chord

```
6  5  4  3  2  1
        ①           Frets
                     1st
   ②        ③ ④      2nd
                     3rd
                     4th
                     5th
```

that there is a new version of the **G** chord to learn. It would be quite correct to play this song using the old 'G Shape' but try the new one and see how it gives the chord a completely different 'flavour'. To recap, the two are completely interchangeable and whenever you see a **G** chord symbol you can try both shapes and see which sound you prefer. It's all good practice.

The other new point to learn is how to 'damp' the strings. In bars 13 to 17 you'll see the 2nd, 3rd, and 4th beats are marked 'damped'. To do this simply rest the side of your hand lightly on the strings just before they cross the bridge and you'll find it gives a nice 'chunky' sound.

The first tune you're going to learn in the second book of the series is that smash hit for Paul Young 'Come Back And Stay'. You'll recognise the names of all the chords you're using from Book 1 but you will also see

The opposite to damped is 'open', which means let the strings ring.

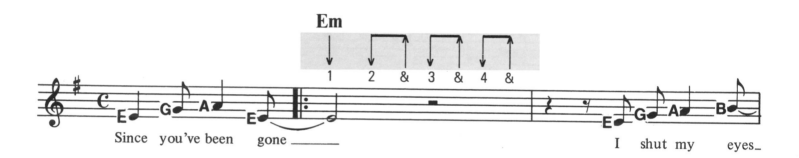

Since you've been gone ____ I shut my eyes_

____ and I fan - ta - sise ____ that you're here with

me. Will you ev - er re - turn? ____

I won't be sat - is - fied ____ 'till you're by my side ____

Come Back And Stay   Continued

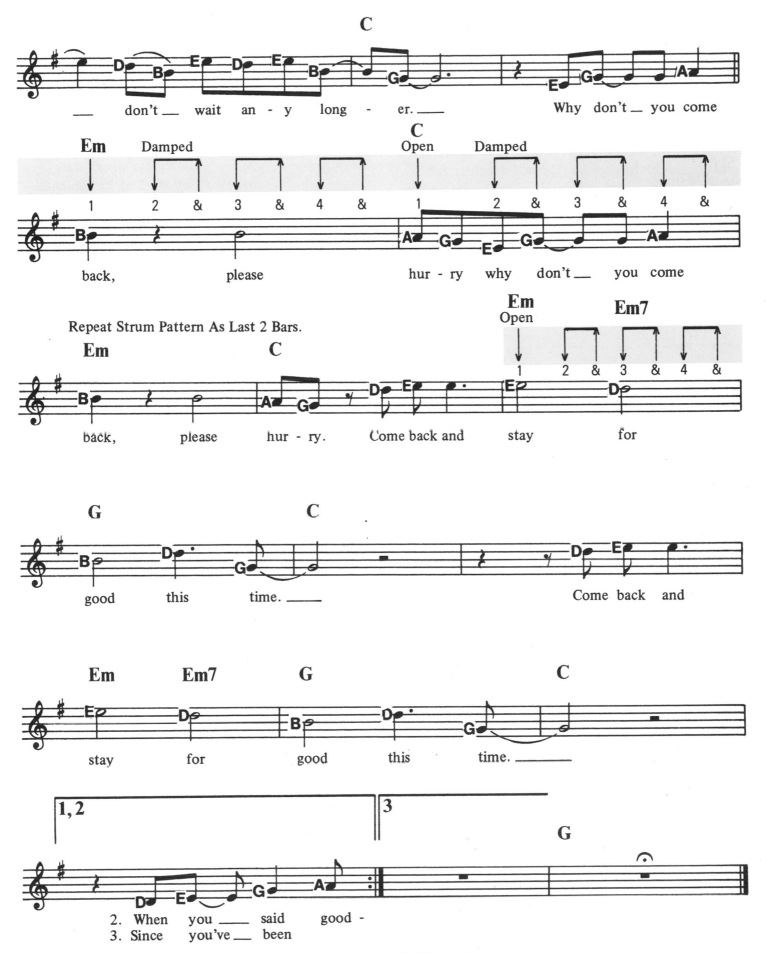

N.B. The full lyric for each song can be found at the back of the book.

Moonlight Shadow

Words & Music: Mike Oldfield

This classic from Mike Oldfield also uses easy chords from Book One. Apart from being a great little song it is a very good practice piece.

Before you start, have a quick look at the middle section ('I stay . . .' etc.). You'll find there's a quick change between the **D** and the **G** chords. In the same section you'll also find very effective semiquaver strums at the end of some of the bars. You'll recognise the effect immediately: it's part of every Rock 'n' Pop guitarist's repertoire.

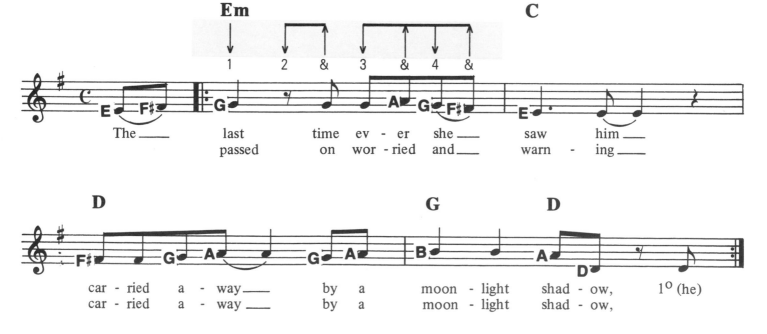

The ___ last time ev - er she ___ saw him ___
passed on wor - ried and ___ warn - ing ___

car - ried a - way ___ by a moon - light shad - ow, 1° (he)
car - ried a - way ___ by a moon - light shad - ow,

Moonlight Shadow Continued

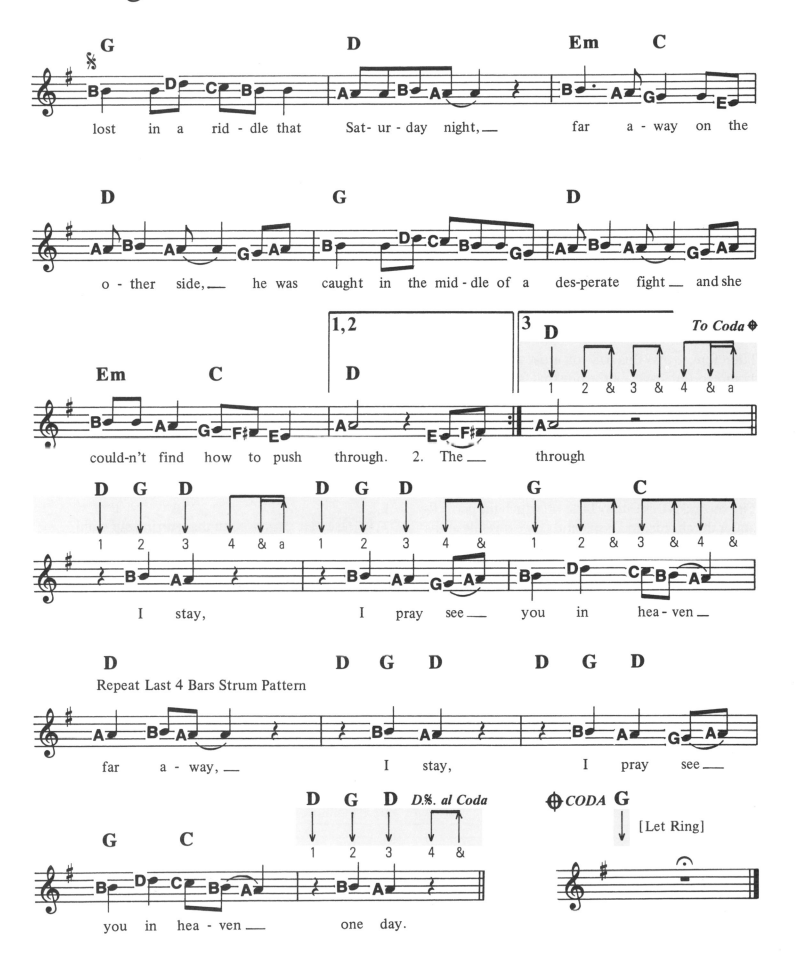

lost in a rid-dle that Sat-ur-day night,— far a-way on the

o-ther side,— he was caught in the mid-dle of a des-perate fight — and she

could-n't find how to push through. 2. The — through

I stay, I pray see — you in hea-ven —

Repeat Last 4 Bars Strum Pattern

far a-way, — I stay, I pray see —

you in hea-ven — one day.

N.B. The full lyric for each song can be found at the back of the book.

Hey Joe   Words & Music: William M. Roberts

This next song is important because, once mastered, it will be a landmark in your progress.

There are two new points to learn. The first is the tie sign, ⌒ which you read about in the section on musical notation. As you know, it is used to tie two notes of the same pitch together so that only the first of the tied notes is played. The effect of a tie sign between two or more differently pitched notes will be dealt with in later books.

In the example below, which is in fact Bar 3 of 'Hey Joe', the tie sign is applied to strum marks with exactly the same effect.

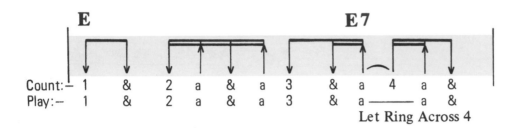

Therefore, to play this bar, you must strum all the marks as shown, but leave out the one that falls directly over the 4 (which you will notice does not have an arrow), letting the previous strum (which is a chord change to **E7**) ring instead. So, to recap, a tie sign means: play the first of the tied notes and let ring, but don't play the second note.

The second is this catchy little riff which fits perfectly under the chords, and is instantly recognisable as the famous bass riff from the Jimi Hendrix smash hit recording of this song. You have seen the tablature explanation at the beginning of this book; well, this is your first chance to use your new ability. It's easy, just remember that the tablature lines represent the 6 strings on the guitar, and let the numbers guide your fingers to the correct fret.

The timing is easy because the riff is a straight eight pattern. Practise it very slowly and evenly before attempting to play it at the correct tempo.

When you have mastered the strum pattern and vocals, try using the riff instead of the chords the second time you play each vocal line.

C   G   D   A   E
Hey Joe where ya goin' with that gun in your hand?
Strum

Hey Joe where ya goin' with that gun in your hand?
Riff ------

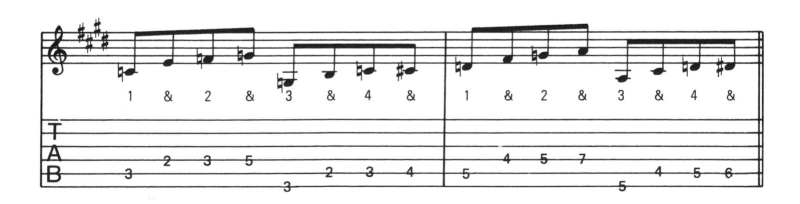

Hey Joe Continued

N.B. The full lyric for each song can be found at the back of the book.

Honky Tonk Women

Words & Music: Mick Jagger and Keith Richards

The **B7** Chord

The **B7** Chord

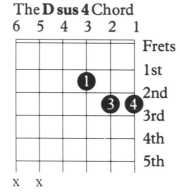

The **D Sus 4** Chord

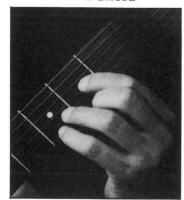

This rhythm and blues classic by The Rolling Stones introduces your first 'sus 4' chord. Without being too technical at this stage, it is sufficient to say that a **'sus 4'** chord contains a note that is not really part of the chord.

Before you go any further, try playing the **'D sus 4'** followed by a normal **D** chord, familiar isn't it? You will find that composers nearly always follow a **'sus 4'** chord with a 'straight' version of the same chord (**D sus 4** to **D** – **A sus 4** to **A**).

The **B7** Chord is self explanatory.

To get the proper effect in bar 3, make the up strokes on the '&' of 3 and the '&' of 4 louder than the other strums. This is called accenting them and is shown in musical notation by putting a ' > ' sign over the top of the note or strum mark.

As a final note remember that

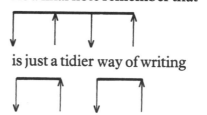

is just a tidier way of writing

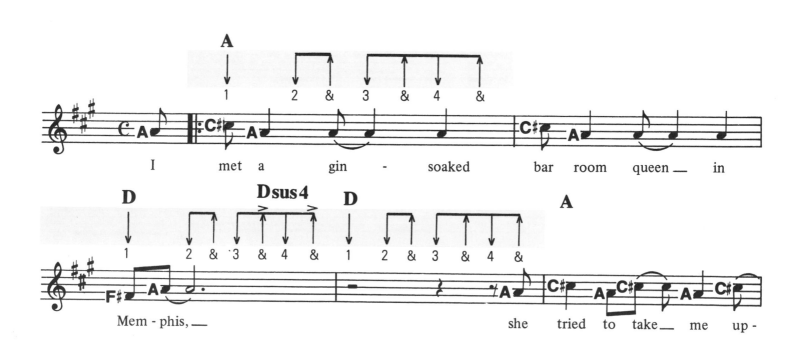

Honky Tonk Women   Continued

N.B. The full lyric for each song can be found at the back of the book.

13

Light My Fire   Words & Music: The Doors

The **B minor 7** Chord

The **Bm7** Chord

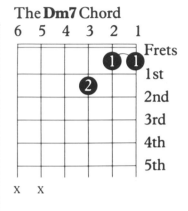

The **D minor 7** Chord

The **Dm7** Chord

This great song has been a hit for several performers. The most famous was the original version by The Doors with Jim Morrison on vocals. It introduces slightly different versions of two chords you learnt in Book One.

As always at this stage, when practising minor sevenths play a straight minor version of the chord first, followed by the minor seventh, and listen to the subtle difference in sound.

The **Dm7** is very simple and needs no explanation, but for the **Bm7** you may need to refer back to the **Bm** shape introduced in Book One.

Simply play a **Bm** and take your little finger off the third string. As long as you're careful that your barré (first finger) is pressing down cleanly across the strings you should now be playing **Bm7**. As this **Bm7** shape does not use any open strings it is 'moveable', just like the **Bm** in Book 1. These two shapes both take their name from the note you are fingering on the fifth string. That is to say if:

The tip of your 1st finger is resting on the 2nd fret of the 5th string, the chord is **B minor 7**.
The tip of your 1st finger is resting on the 3rd fret of the 5th string, the chord is **C minor 7**.
The tip of your 1st finger is resting on the 5th fret of the 5th string, the chord is **D minor 7**.

Light My Fire   Continued

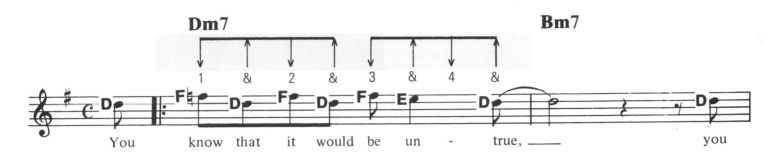

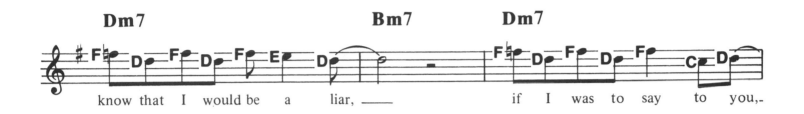

You know that it would be un - true, _____ you

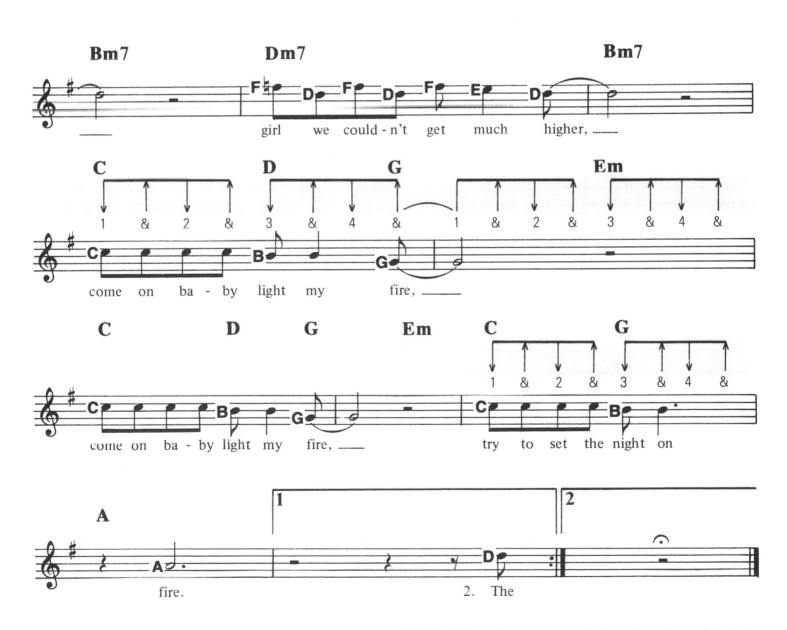

know that I would be a liar, _____ if I was to say to you,_

_____ girl we could - n't get much higher, _____

come on ba - by light my fire, _____

come on ba - by light my fire, _____ try to set the night on

fire.   2. The

N.B. The full lyric for each song can be found at the back of the book.

So Far Away
Words & Music: Mark Knopfler

This Dire Straits hit is a song of contrasts, and since you know all the necessary chords, you should be able to concentrate your attention on a performance with 'light and shade'.

For the verse, damp the strings with the side of your right hand (as in 'Come Back & Stay' earlier in the book), then strum only the bass strings of the chord for that 'chunky' sound.

There is a 'magic moment' where in bar 8, on a count of "4 &" you see the "open" instruction. Remove your damping hand for the quick down up ' ⌐⌐ ' and change chord to G, letting the strings ring 'open' and the whole song 'open up'.

Here is the full strum pattern for bars 8 and 9.

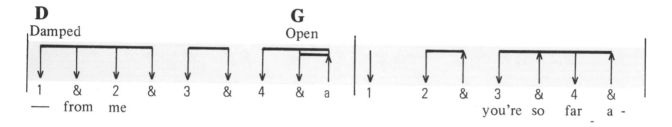

VERSE

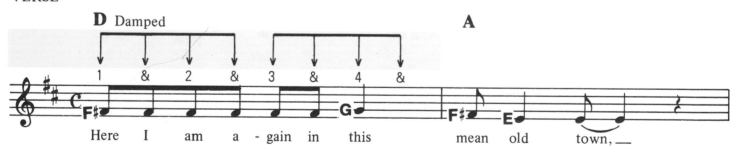

So Far Away   Continued

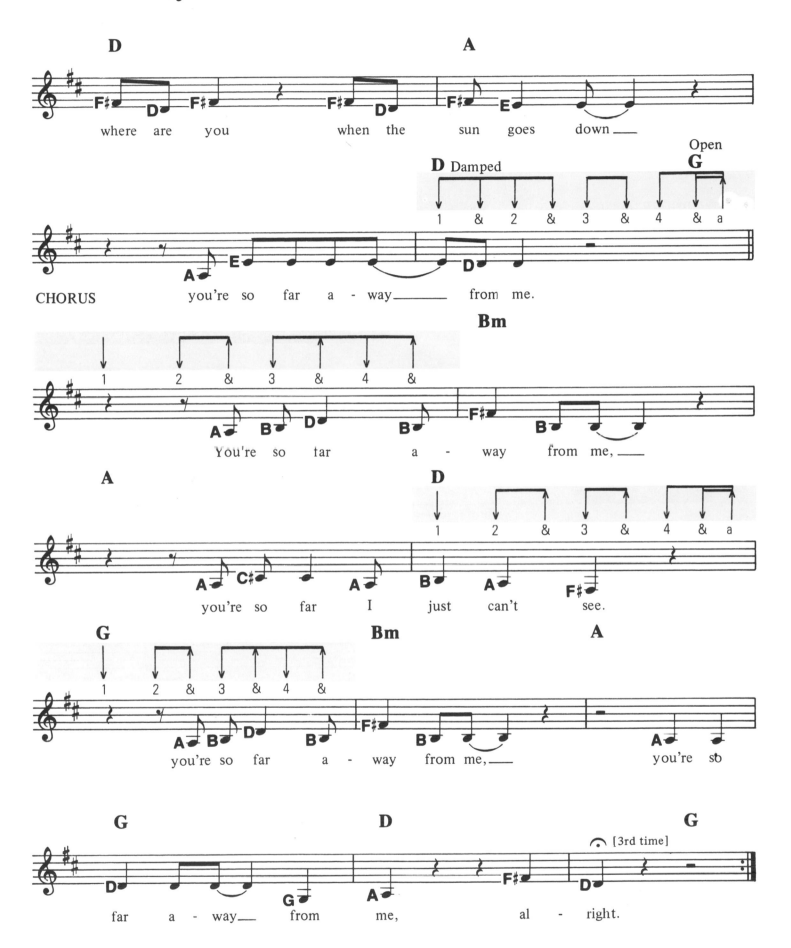

N.B. The full lyric for each song can be found at the back of the book.

I Shot The Sheriff   Words & Music: Bob Marley

INTRO RIFF

Eric Clapton had a smash hit with this Bob Marley song. The notation and tablature above give you the great little figure that goes in the last four bars before you go back to the beginning (D.C.). The strumming pattern introduces an interesting new effect, look at the first bar and I'll explain what happens.

The sign E you encountered in the first book, means you hit the bottom E string only. The strumming on beats 2 and 4 is as normal, but on beat 3 you will see the sign ✕. In this instance it means that you hit all six strings with the side of your right hand, it should produce a percussive 'clicky' sound. This is a very effective reggae type rhythm and a little time spent on it will reproduce a really fantastic effect. Do exactly the same for the **A** minor chord playing the open A string on the first beat.

I Shot The Sheriff　Continued

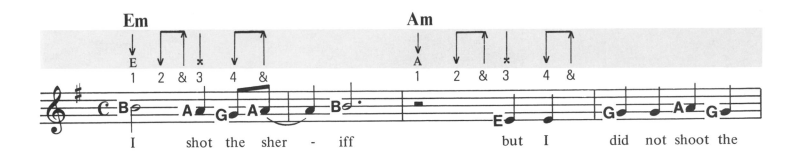

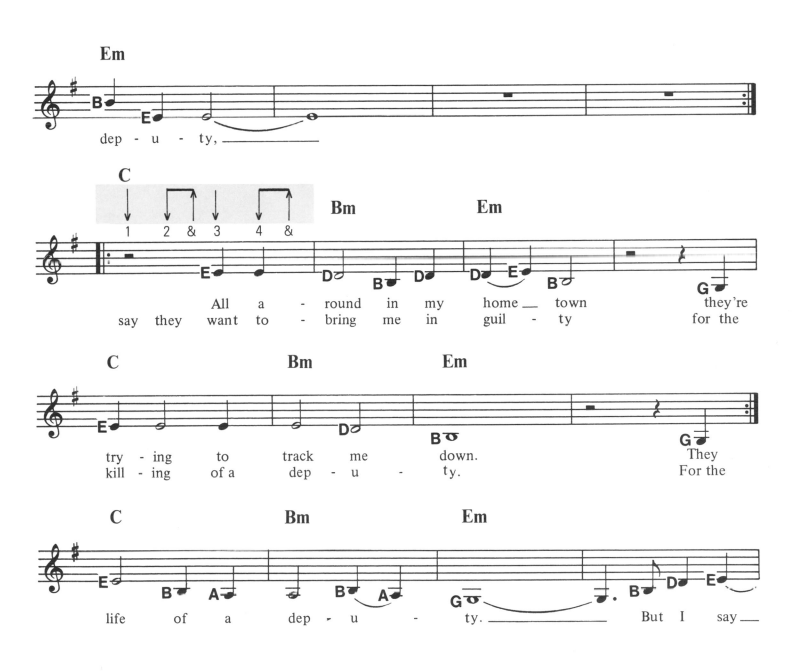

I shot the sher - iff　　but I　did not shoot the

dep - u - ty, ____

All a - round in my home ___ town　　they're

say they want to - bring me in　guil - ty　　for the

try - ing　to　　track me　　down.　They

kill - ing of a　dep - u - ty.　For the

life　of a　dep - u - ty. ____　But I　say ___

Riff As In Tablature

D.C.

N.B. The full lyric for each song can be found at the back of the book.

(This Could Be) The Last Time

Words & Music: Mick Jagger and Keith Richards

You will be familiar with the chords for this rock classic by The Rolling Stones so you will be able to concentrate on learning to play the neat little 'riff' which is written above in both notation and tablature.

Play the two bar phrase twice as an introduction. You'll also find it fits very nicely in bars 3 and 4 and 7 and 8 of the verse. Note that bar numbers should be counted from the thick Double Bar Line

If you just want to strum through these bars simply follow the chord symbols as usual.

When playing the second half of Bar 2 of the above phrase, the plectrum (or fingers of the right hand) has to 'jump' the third string. Don't worry if you can't stop it from sounding, it fits in with the chord. However, if you want it to sound exactly like the original, practise until you can play it as it's written.

(This Could Be) The Last Time Continued

N.B. The full lyric for each song can be found at the back of the book.

Don't Pay The Ferryman
Words & Music: Chris de Burgh

The **D/F♯** Chord

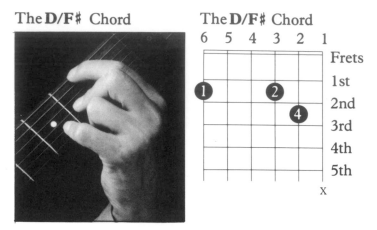

The **D/F♯** Chord

This song has a chord of **D** with an F♯ in the bass which is written **D/F♯**. Try it and hear the rich resonance.

The strum pattern for this Chris De Burgh hit is familiar to you but take note that the **D** and **D/F♯** are both 'accented' (as explained in 'Honky Tonk Women'). The **D** arrives on the last 'up strum' at the end of the bar that goes '…RAIN came DOWN'. Similarly the **D/F♯** arrives on the last 'up strum' at the end of the bar that goes '…WILD dog HOWL'. This is a great effect and again is instantly recognisable from the hit record.

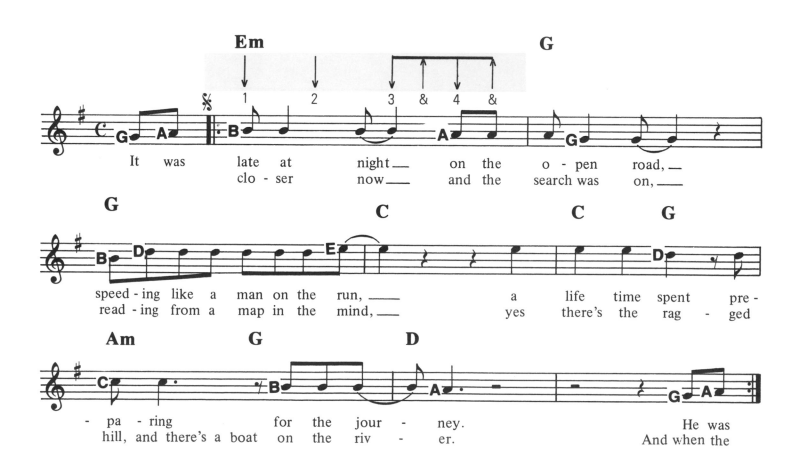

It was late at night on the o - pen road, —
clo - ser now and the search was on, —

speed - ing like a man on the run, — a life time spent pre-
read - ing from a map in the mind, — yes there's the rag - ged

- pa - ring for the jour - ney. He was
hill, and there's a boat on the riv - er. And when the

Don't Pay The Ferryman Continued

N.B. The full lyric for each song can be found at the back of the book.

My Sweet Lord
Words & Music: George Harrison

The G♯ dim Chord

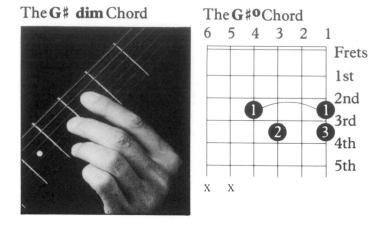

The G♯° Chord

'My Sweet Lord', written and recorded by George Harrison, was a big hit all over the world.

You only have to learn one new chord and it's one with a very interesting property. The chord is **G♯** diminished but this is usually written as **G♯ °**, the circle being a 'musical shorthand' method of writing 'diminished'. (It could also be written **G♯ dim**).

You'll see that it's a four-string chord with all the strings you are striking 'stopped' by the left hand and you know by now that means it's moveable.

At this point go back and re-read the section on **Bm7** which occurs in 'Light My Fire'. Then come back to this and you'll learn something very interesting.

Checked it out? O.K. read on.

You discovered that you can move that minor 7th shape up and down the fret board and it always takes its name from the note fingered on the fifth string. Well, the unusual fact about the diminished chord is that it can take its name from any of the notes stopped with the left hand. That means that although in this instance we have called the shape **G♯ °**, it could also be called **D°**, **B°**, or **F°**.

This will be explained in Book 3.

My ___ sweet Lord ___

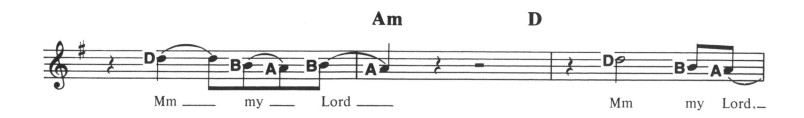

Mm ___ my ___ Lord ___   Mm   my   Lord, ___

My Sweet Lord Continued

N.B. The full lyric for each song can be found at the back of the book.

A Whiter Shade Of Pale

Words & Music: Keith Reid & Gary Brooker

The **F** Chord

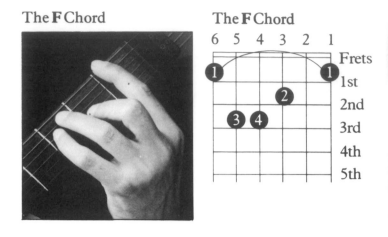

The **F** Chord

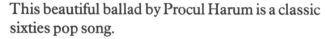

This beautiful ballad by Procul Harum is a classic sixties pop song.

It will also introduce you to what is probably the most important major chord shape for the guitar. It uses all six strings and is therefore completely moveable. The form shown here is the **F major** required for this piece. Try making the barré right across the neck with the first finger and see if all the notes sound cleanly. Then add the second, third and fourth fingers. By now you shouldn't have any trouble with this shape.

It is worth pointing out at this stage that this chord is simply a version of the **E** chord you learnt at the

beginning of Book 1. The first finger barré is actually replacing the 'nut' of the guitar. Try it and see! You won't need chord boxes for the two other new symbols – they're just different versions of what you already know.

G/B means the new **G** chord that you learnt for 'Come Back and Stay' with a B note at the bottom. Finger your original **G** shape, leave off the second finger and play the top five strings only. For the **Am7** simply play your basic **A minor** position and remove your third finger.

It gets easier all the time, doesn't it?

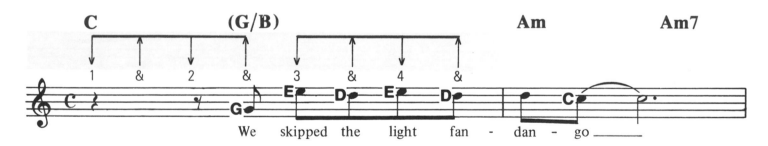

We skipped the light fan - dan - go

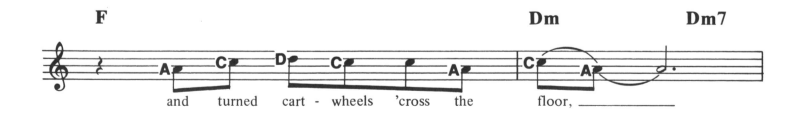

and turned cart - wheels 'cross the floor,

I was feel - ing kind of sea - sick, ___ but the crowd called out for

A Whiter Shade Of Pale Continued

more. _____ The room was hum - ming hard - er,

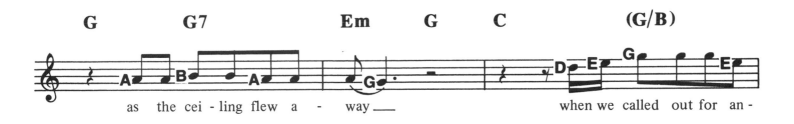

as the cei - ling flew a - way _____ when we called out for an-

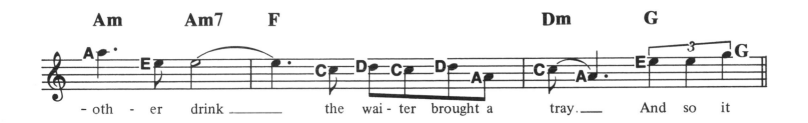

- oth - er drink _____ the wai - ter brought a tray. _____ And so it

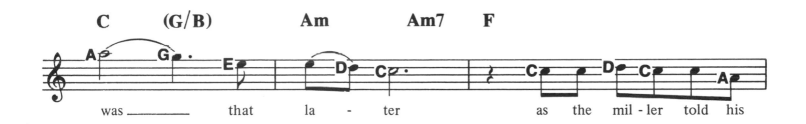

was _____ that la - ter as the mil - ler told his

tale, _____ that her face at first just

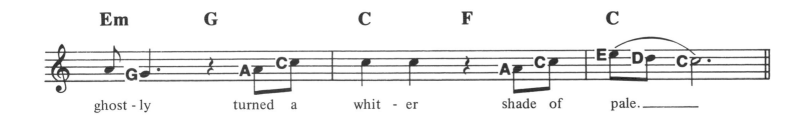

ghost - ly turned a whit - er shade of pale. _____

N.B. The full lyric for each song can be found at the back of the book.

The Wild Boys

Words & Music: Duran Duran

You've come across all the effects and chords used in this big hit by Duran Duran. Just keep your foot tapping and watch out for the changes in the strumming pattern.

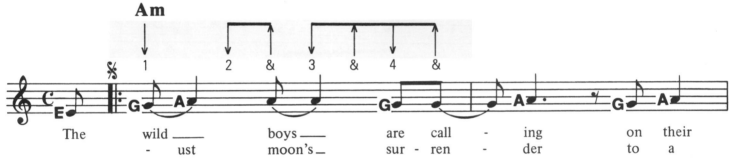

The wild ___ boys ___ are call - ing on their
- ust moon's ___ sur - ren - der to a

way back from the fire ___ 1° (in Aug -) wild boys fal - len far ___
dust cloud on the rise ___

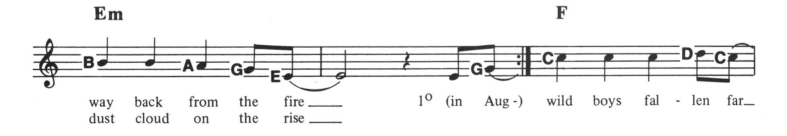

___ from glo - ry, reck - less and so hung - ered, on the

ra - zor's edge you trail, ___ be - cause there's mur - der by the

The Wild Boys   Continued

N.B. The full lyric for each song can be found at the back of the book.

Nights in White Satin

Words & Music: Justin Hayward

This song by The Moody Blues introduces you to a fast waltz tempo. It could have been written in a different form but at this stage this is the simplest way to present it.

Nights in White Satin Continued

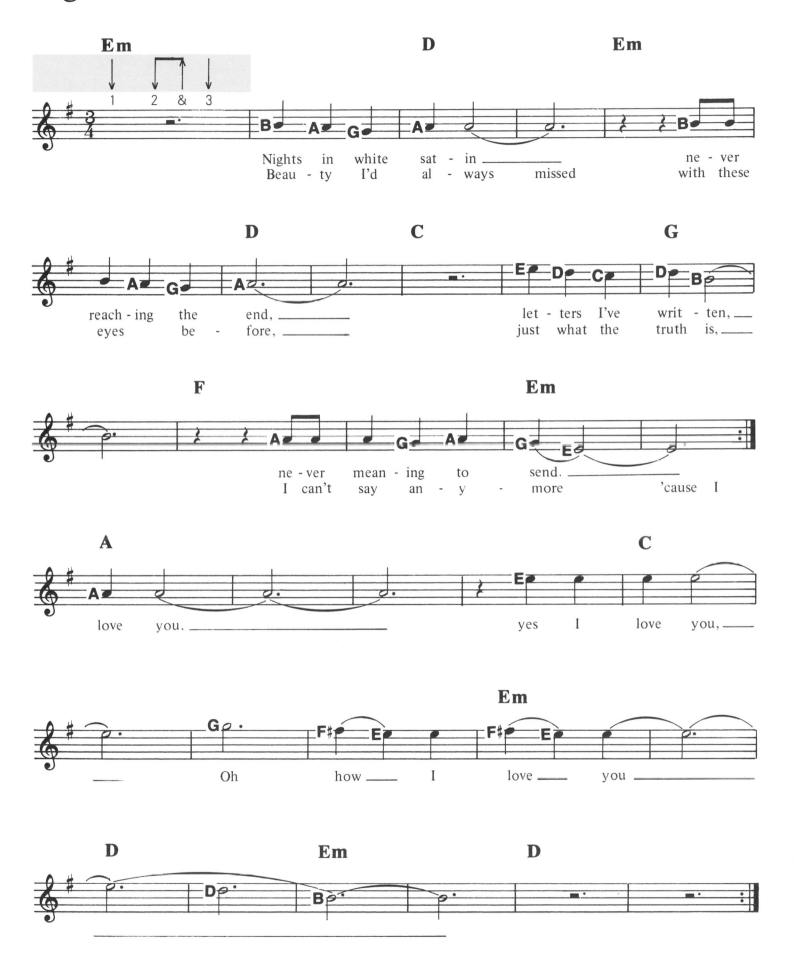

N.B. The full lyric for each song can be found at the back of the book.

31

Hungry Like The Wolf

Words & Music: Duran Duran

The E Sus 4 Chord

The E sus 4 Chord

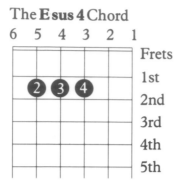

You need only one new chord to play this Duran Duran song, and it's a simple variation of one you already know.

Simply play your basic **E** chord shape and place your fourth finger on the second fret, third string, as shown above. There is no need to remove your first finger from the string while you do this; it does not have any effect while the little finger is stopping the string and it makes changing between the chords so much simpler.

A very basic explanation of **'sus 4'** chords was given when they were first introduced in 'Honky Tonk Women'.

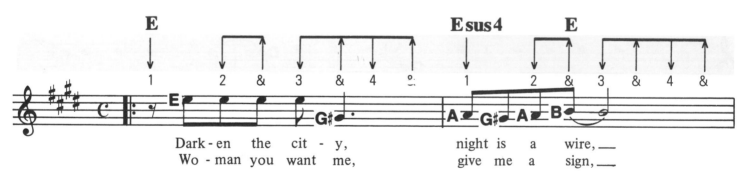

Dark - en the cit - y, night is a wire, ___
Wo - man you want me, give me a sign, ___

steam in the sub - way, earth is a fire, ___ } do do
and catch my breath - ing even clo - ser be - hind ___ }

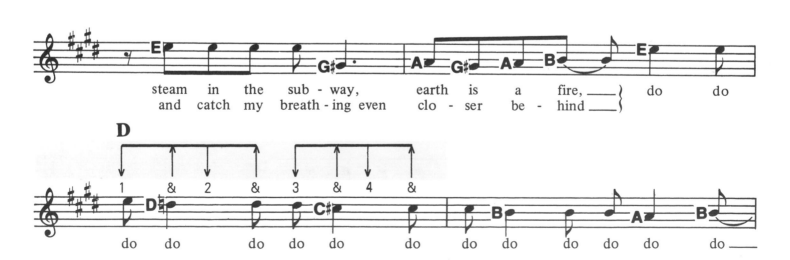

do do do do do do do do do do do do ___

Hungry Like The Wolf Continued

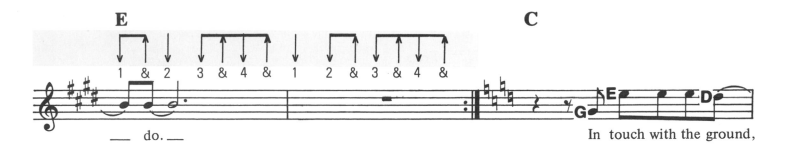

do.   In touch with the ground,

I'm on the hunt __ I'm aft - er you. __ Smell like I sound,__

I'm lost in a crowd, __ and __ I'm hung - ry like __ the wolf.__

Strad-dle the line __ in dis - cord and rhyme, __ I'm on the hunt__

I'm aft - er you. __ Mouth is a - live __ with jui - ces like wine__

and __ I'm hung - ry like __ the wolf.__

N.B. The full lyric for each song can be found at the back of the book.

While My Guitar Gently Weeps

Words & Music: George Harrison

The **F♯m** Chord

6 5 4 3 2 1

The **C♯m** Chord

6 5 4 3 2 1

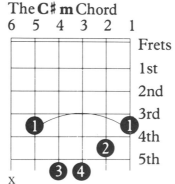

Frets
1st
2nd
3rd
4th
5th

George Harrison wrote this beautiful ballad which appeared on The Beatles' 'White album'.

Two new chords appear at this stage but they are very similar to shapes you have already learnt. For the **F♯m,** start by playing your six string **F** chord and then move it up one fret. Having done this, remove your second

finger from the third string and there you have it **F♯m** minor.

Similarly, to play **C♯m** make your familiar **Bm** shape and move it up two frets. There are diagrams for you if this is not clear but by now moveable chords should present no problem.

34

While My Guitar Gently Weeps   Continued

N.B. The full lyric for each song can be found at the back of the book.

35

Pinball Wizard

Words & Music: Peter Townshend

The **A Sus 4** Chord

The **A sus 4** Chord

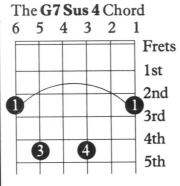

The **G7 Sus 4** Chord

The **G7 Sus 4** Chord

This hit by The Who was taken from their opera 'Tommy' and features one of Pete Townshend's classic chord progressions. There are three new **'Sus 4'** chords for this piece but you have only been given two of them. The reason for this is that the **G7 sus 4** shape is a moveable chord and to play **F7 sus 4** you simply move it two frets down the fretboard. This should not need any further explanation but if you are in any difficulty read the section on the **F** chord which was introduced in 'A Whiter Shade Of Pale.'

The rhythm for the verse is much simpler than it looks, and you will soon recognise the phrase. The figure in bars 9 and 11 is another very common pattern. Just remember to tap your foot on 1,2,3,4 and play the chords on the '&'.

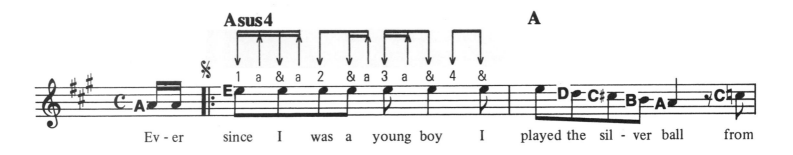

Ev - er since I was a young boy I played the sil - ver ball from

So - ho down to Brigh - ton, I must have played em' all, but I

ain't seen no - thing like him in an - y a - muse - ment hall, that

Pinball Wizard Continued

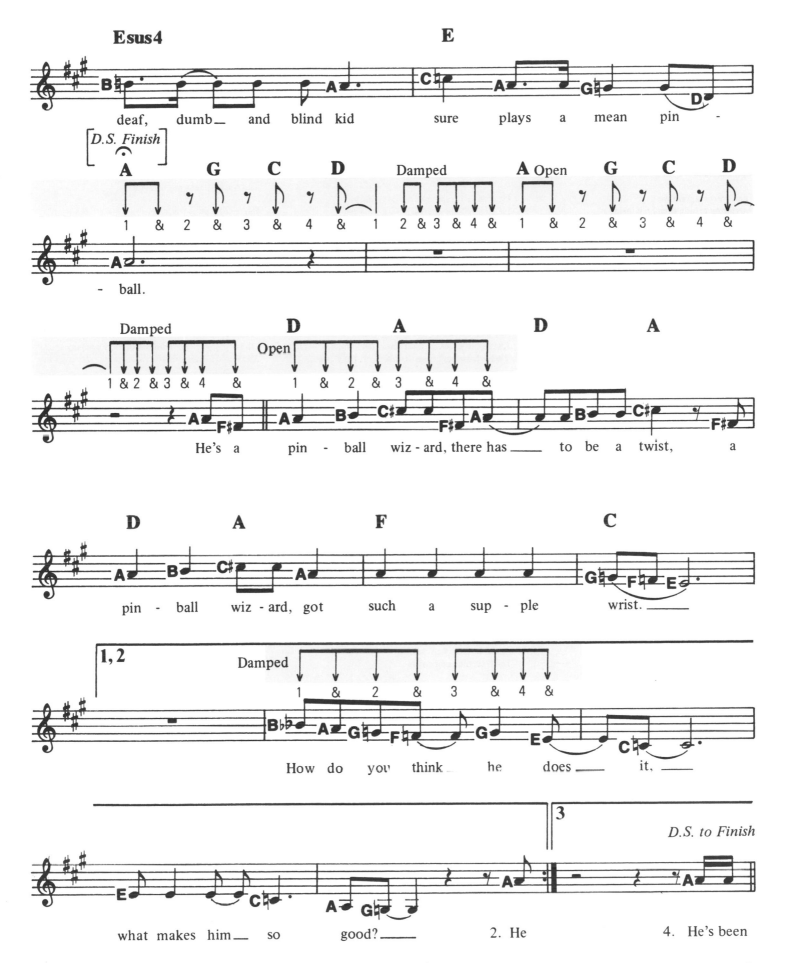

N.B. The full lyric for each song can be found at the back of the book.

Come Back And Stay

Since you've been gone
I shut my eyes
And I fantasise
That you're here with me.
Will you ever return?
I won't be satisfied till you're by my side.
Don't wait any longer
Why don't you come back, please hurry.
Why don't you come back, please hurry,
Come back and stay for good this time,
Come back and stay for good this time.

When you said goodbye
I was trying to hide what I felt inside
Until it passed me by.
You said you'd return,
You said that you'd be mine till the end of time.
Well don't wait any longer.

Since you've been gone
I opened my eyes and I realised
What we had together.
Will you ever return?
Or have you changed your mind, if you wanna stay mine
Just love me forever.

Moonlight Shadow

The last time ever she saw him carried away by a
     moonlight shadow,
He passed on worried and warning carried away by a
     moonlight shadow,
Lost in a riddle that Saturday night far away on the other
     side
He was caught in the middle of a desperate fight,
And she couldn't find how to push through.

The trees that whisper in the evening
Carried away by a moonlight shadow
Sing a song of sorrow and grieving
Carried away by a moonlight shadow.
All she saw was the silhouette of a gun
Far away on the other side
He was shot six times by a man on the run
And she couldn't find how to push it through.

Four a.m. in the morning
Carried away by a moonlight shadow
I watch your vision forming
Carried away by a moonlight shadow.
The stars move slowly in a silvery light
Far away on the other side
Will you come to talk to me this night
But she couldn't find how to push through.

I stay, I pray see you in heaven far away,
I stay, I pray see you in heaven one day.

Caught in the middle of a hundred and five
The night was heavy and the air was alive
But she couldn't find how to push through.

Hey Joe

Hey Joe, where ya goin' with that gun in your hand?
I said hey Joe, where ya goin' with that gun in your hand?
I'm going out to find my woman now.
She's been runnin' round with some other man.
I said I'm going out and find my woman
She's been runnin' round with some other man.

Hey Joe, tell me what are you gonna do?
Hey Joe, tell me what are you gonna do?
Well I guess I'll shoot my woman, that's what I'll do.
Well I guess I'll shoot 'em both before I'm through.

Hey Joe, tell me where are you gonna go?
Hey Joe, tell me where are you gonna go?
Well, I think I'll go down to my favourite place, Mexico
Well, I think I'll go down to where a man can be free
And there ain't gonna be no hangman's ropes
Gonna be put around me.

Honky Tonk Women

I met a gin soaked, bar-room queen in Memphis,
She tried to take me upstairs for a ride,
She had to heave me right across her shoulder
'Cause I just can't seem to drink you off my mind.

Chorus:

It's the Honky Tonk Women
Gimme, gimme, gimme the honky tonk blues.

I played a divorceé in New York City
I had to put up some kind of a fight.
The lady then she covered me with roses,
She blew my nose and then she blew my mind.

Chorus

Light My Fire

You know that it would be untrue,
You know that I would be a liar
If I was to say to you
Girl, we couldn't get much higher.

Chorus:
Come on, baby, light my fire.
Come on, baby, light my fire.
Try to set the night on fire.

The time to hesitate is through,
No time to wallow in the mire,
Try now we can only lose
And our love become a funeral pyre.

Chorus.

So Far Away

Here I am again in this mean old town,
And you're so far away from me.
Now where are you when the sun goes down
You're so far away from me.
I'm tired of being in love and being all alone
When you're so far away from me.
I'm tired of making out on the telephone
'Cause you're so far away from me.
And I get so tired when I have to explain
When you're so far away from me.
See you've been in the sun and I've been in the rain
And you're so far away from me.

You're so far away from me,
You're so far I just can't see.
You're so far away from me,
You're so far away from me, alright,
You're so far away from me.
(Fade)

I Shot The Sheriff

I shot the sheriff, but I did not shoot the deputy.
I shot the sheriff, but I did not shoot the deputy.
All around in my hometown they're trying to track me
     down.
They say they want to bring me in guilty for the killing of
     a deputy.
For the killing of a deputy, but I say:

I shot the sheriff but I swear it was in self-defence.
I shot the sheriff and they say it is a capital offence.
Sheriff John Brown always hated me: for what, I don't
     know
Every time that I plant a seed he said kill it before it grow.
He said kill it before it grow, but I say:

I shot the sheriff but I swear it was in self-defence.
I shot the sheriff but I swear it was in self-defence.
Freedom came my way one day and I started out of town.
All of a sudden I see Sheriff John Brown aiming to shoot
     me down,
So I shot, I shot him down, but I say:

I shot the sheriff but I did not shoot the deputy.
I shot the sheriff but I did not shoot no deputy.
Reflexes got the better of me and what is to be must be.
Every day the bucket goes to the well but one day the
     bottom will drop out,
Yes, one day the bottom will drop out, but I say:

(Rpt. verse 1 and fade)

(This Could Be) The Last Time

Well, I told you once and I told you twice,
But you never listen to my advice,
You don't try very hard to please me,
With what you know it should be easy.

This could be the last time,
This could be the last time,
May be the last time
I don't know, Oh no, Oh no.

Well, I'm sorry girl but I can't stay
Feelin' like I do today.
It's too much pain and too much sorrow,
Guess I'll feel the same tomorrow.

Well, I told you once and I told you twice,
That someone else will have to pay the price.
But here's a chance to change your mind,
'Cause I'll be gone a long, long time.

Don't Pay The Ferryman

It was late at night on the open road,
Speeding like a man on the run,
A life time spent preparing for the journey.
He was closer now and the search was on,
Reading from a map in the mind.
Yes, there's the ragged hill, and there's a boat on the
river.

And when the rain came down
He heard a wild dog howl.
There were voices in the night.
(Don't do it!)
Voices out of sight,
(Don't do it!)
Too many men have failed before,
Whatever you do
Don't pay the ferryman,
Don't even fix a price.
Don't pay the ferryman
Until he gets you to the other side.

In the roaming mist then he gets on board,
Now there'll be no turning back,
Beware the hooded old man at the rudder.
And then the lightning flashed and the thunder roared,
And people calling out his name,
And dancing bows that jabbered and a' moaned on the
water.
And then the ferryman said there is trouble ahead
So you must pay me now
(Don't do it!)
You must pay me now
(Don't do it!)
And still that voice came through the air
Whatever you do...

My Sweet Lord

My sweet Lord, mm my Lord, mm my Lord,
I really want to see you.
Really want to be with you.
Really want to see you Lord,
But it takes so long, my Lord.

My sweet Lord, mm my Lord, mm my Lord,
I really want to know you.
Really want to go with you.
Really want to show you, Lord,
That it won't take long, my Lord.

My sweet Lord, mm my Lord, my sweet Lord,
I really want to see you.
Really want to see you.
Really want to see you Lord.
Really want to see you, Lord,
But it takes so long my Lord,
My sweet Lord, mm my Lord, my, my, my Lord, my
    sweet Lord.

A Whiter Shade Of Pale

We skipped the light fandango and turned cartwheels
    'cross the floor
I was feeling kind of seasick
But the crowd called out for more,
The room was humming harder
As the ceiling flew away
When we called out for another drink
The waiter brought a tray.
And so it was that later
As the miller told his tale
That her face at first just ghostly turned a whiter shade
    of pale.

The Wild Boys

The wild boys are calling
On their way back from the fire,
In August moon's surrender
To a dust cloud on the rise.
Wild boys fallen far from glory,
Reckless and so hungered,
On the razor's edge you trail,
Because there's murder by the roadside
In a sore afraid new world.
They tried to break us,
Looks like they'll try again.

Chorus:
Wild boys never lose it,
Wild boys never choose this way.
Wild boys never close your eyes,
Wild boys always shine.

You got sirens for a welcome,
There's bloodstain for your pain,
And your telephone's been ringing
While you're dancing in the rain.
Wild boys wonder where is glory,
Where is all you angels,
Now the figureheads have fell.
And lovers war with arrows
Over secrets they could tell.
They tried to tame you,
Looks like they'll try again..

Chorus.

Nights In White Satin

Nights in white satin never reaching the end.
Letters I've written never meaning to send.
Beauty I'd always missed with these eyes before,
Just what the truth is I can't say any more,
'Cause I love you,
Yes I love
Oh, how I love you

Gazing at people, some hand in hand,
Just what I'm going through they can't understand.
Some try to tell me thoughts they cannot defend,
Just what you want to be, you'll be in the end,
And I love you,
Yes, I love you,
Oh, how I love you.
How I love you.

Hungry Like The Wolf

Darken the city, night is a wire,
Steam in the subway, earth is a fire,
Do do do do do do do do
Do do do do do do do.

Woman you want me, give me a sign,
And catch my breathing even closer behind
Do do do...
Do do do...

Chorus:
In touch with the ground, I'm on the hunt, I'm after you,
Smell like I sound, I'm lost in a crowd,
And I'm hungry like the wolf
Straddle the line in discord and rhyme
I'm on the hunt, I'm after you.
Mouth is alive with juices like wine
And I'm hungry like the wolf.

Stalked in the forest, too close to hide,
I'll be upon you by the moonlight side,
Do do do...
High blood drumming on the skin, it's so tight,
You feel my heat, I'm just a moment behind
Do do do...

Chorus:
In touch with the ground, I'm on the hunt I'm after you
Scent and a sound, I'm lost and I'm found,
And I'm hungry like the wolf
Strut on a line, it's discord and rhyme
I howl and I whine, I'm after you.
Mouth is alive, all running inside
And I'm hungry like the wolf.

Final Chorus:
I break from the crowd, I'm on the hunt, I'm after you.
I smell like I sound, I'm lost and I'm found
And I'm hungry like the wolf.
Strut on a line, it's discord and rhyme
Mouth is alive with juices like wine
And I'm hungry like the wolf.

And I'm hungry like the wolf.

While My Guitar Gently Weeps

I look at you all see the love there that's sleeping
While my guitar gently weeps
I look at the floor and I see it needs sweeping
Still my guitar gently weeps
I don't know why nobody told you how to unfold your
    love
I don't know how someone controlled you they bought
    and sold you
I look at you all see the love there that's sleeping
While my guitar gently weeps
I look at you all
Still my guitar gently weeps.

I look at the world and I notice it's turning
While my guitar gently weeps
With every mistake we must surely be learning
Still my guitar gently weeps
I don't know how you were diverted you were perverted
    too
I don't know how you were inverted no one altered you
I look at you all see the love there that's sleeping
While my guitar gently weeps
I look at you all
Still my guitar gently weeps.

Pinball Wizard

Ever since I was a young boy I played the silver ball;
From Soho down to Brighton I must have played 'em all,
But I ain't seen nothin' like him in any amusement hall.
That deaf, dumb and blind kid sure plays a mean
    pinball.

Chorus:
He's a pinball wizard there has to be a twist,
A pinball wizard, got such a supple wrist
How do you think he does it? (I don't know)
What makes him so good?

He stands like a statue, becomes part of the machine,
Feelin' all the bumpers, always playin' clean,
Plays by intuition, the digit counters fall
That deaf, dumb and blind kid sure plays a mean
    pinball.

Chorus.

Ain't got no distractions, can't hear no buzzes and bells,
Don't see no lights a flashin' plays by sense of smell,
Always gets a replay never seen him fall.
That deaf, dumb and blind kid sure plays a mean
    pinball.

I thought I was the body table king,
But I just handed my pinball crown to him.
How do you think he does it? (I don't know)
What makes him so good?

He's been on my fav'rite table, he can beat my best,
His disciples lead him in and he just does the rest.
He's got crazy flippin' fingers, never seen him fall
That deaf, dumb and blind kid sure plays a mean
    pinball.

10/95 (22792)